# THE REVENGE
# OF THE BABY-SAT

## Other Books by Bill Watterson

*Calvin and Hobbes*
*Something Under the Bed Is Drooling*
*Yukon Ho!*
*Weirdos From Another Planet!*

## Treasury Collections

*The Essential Calvin and Hobbes*
*The Calvin and Hobbes Lazy Sunday Book*
*The Authoritative Calvin and Hobbes*

# THE REVENGE OF THE BABY-SAT

# A Calvin and Hobbes Collection by Bill Watterson

SCHOLASTIC INC.
New York Toronto London Auckland Sydney

*Calvin and Hobbes* is distributed internationally by Universal Press Syndicate.

ISBN 0-590-45218-5

12 11 10 9 8 7 6 5 4 3 2 1                                                                                        9/0

Printed in the U.S.A.                                                           40

First Scholastic printing, September 1991

Printed on recycled paper.

WHO MADE THIS MESS OUT HERE?!

IT WASN'T *ME*, MOM! IT WAS...UH.. IT WAS...

IT WAS A HORRIBLE LITTLE VENUSIAN WHO MATERIALIZED IN THE KITCHEN! HE TOOK OUT SOME DIABOLICAL HIGH-FREQUENCY DEVICE, POINTED IT AT VARIOUS OBJECTS, AND...

MOTHERS ARE THE NECESSITY OF INVENTION.

I'M HO-OME!

VAPOK

WHAT DID YOU DO, STEP ON A LAND MINE?

WHEN'S DAD EVER GOING TO BUILD THAT TIGER PIT I KEEP ASKING HIM ABOUT?

CALVIN, WHERE ARE YOU? GET OUT HERE!

COME ON, CALVIN, I'M GETTING TIRED OF THIS!

I *MEAN* IT, CALVIN! COME OUT AND TAKE YOUR BATH! *NOW!*

SOONER OR LATER SHE'S GOING TO HAVE TO QUESTION WHETHER THIS IS REALLY WORTH THE TROUBLE.

# CALViN and HOBBES
by WATTERSON

IF *I* WAS IN CHARGE, WE'D NEVER SEE GRASS BETWEEN OCTOBER AND MAY.

ON "THREE", READY? ONE... TWO... THREE!

SNOW!

I SAID SNOW! C'MON! SNOW!

**SNOW!**

OK THEN, *DON'T* SNOW! SEE WHAT *I* CARE! I *LIKE* THIS WEATHER! LET'S HAVE IT FOREVER!

*PLEEAASE* SNOW! PLEASE?? JUST A FOOT! OK, EIGHT INCHES! THAT'S ALL! C'MON! SIX INCHES, EVEN! HOW ABOUT JUST SIX??

I'M *WAAIIITING...*

RRRRGGHHH

DO YOU WANT ME TO BECOME AN ATHEIST?

WATTERSON

SPIFF'S SPACECRAFT IS IMMOBILIZED! THE NAVIGA-TRON HAS SHORTED OUT!

A ZILLION MILES FROM ANY PLANET, OUR HERO MUST CLIMB OUT AND FIX IT HIMSELF IN ZERO GRAVITY!

UPSIDE DOWN, SPIFF CLINGS TIGHTLY TO HIS SPACESHIP! ONE SLIP WILL SEND HIM HURLING INTO THE HORRORS OF THE INFINITE BEYOND!

GO...TO... SCHOOL!

NO!

I DON'T UNDERSTAND HOW SANTA RUNS HIS OPERATION. HOW CAN HE AFFORD TO GIVE TOYS AWAY?

HOW DOES HE PAY FOR THE RAW MATERIALS HE USES TO MAKE THE TOYS? HOW DOES HE PAY HIS ELVES?

THERE'S NO INCOME TO COVER HIS COSTS. HOW DOES HE DO IT?

DEFICIT SPENDING, I GUESS.

SURE, BUT SOONER OR LATER IT'S GOING TO CATCH UP TO HIM, AND THEN WHERE WILL *I* BE?!

DEAR SANTA, Hi, it's me, Calvin. THIS YEAR I'VE BEEN

EXTRA GOOD, SO...

PBTBT!!

MMF MMF EEP!

PERHAPS YOU NEED A DRINK OF WATER.

I THINK I DO.

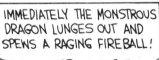

# Calvin and Hobbes

by WATTERSON

AHH... THE PERFECT SLUSHBALL!

HARD ENOUGH TO STING, YET SLOPPY ENOUGH TO DRIBBLE DOWN THE COLLAR AND SOAK THE UNDERGARMENTS.

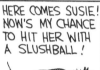

HERE COMES SUSIE! NOW'S MY CHANCE TO HIT HER WITH A SLUSHBALL!

I SEE YOU! YOU'D BETTER NOT THROW THAT! SANTA CLAUS IS WATCHING YOU RIGHT NOW!

FWISSHHH! ZINGG

WHAP!

OH YES! YES! IT WAS WORTH IT! WHAT A SHOT! I'M NOT SORRY! OH, IT WAS BEAUTIFUL! I'D DO IT AGAIN IN A MINUTE! HA HA!

SANTA'S GONNA SKIP THIS BLOCK FOR YEARS.

**Panel 1:** DO YOU THINK MONSTERS ARE UNDER THE BED TONIGHT?

**Panel 2:** I DON'T KNOW. HOW CAN YOU TELL WITHOUT LOOKING?

**Panel 3:** ONE WAY IS TO TELL A STORY ABOUT A LITTLE KID GETTING MAULED AND EATEN ALIVE.

**Panel 4:** HOW DOES *THAT* TELL YOU IF YOU HAVE MONSTERS? / SOMETIMES THEY LAUGH.

**Panel 5:** I'M FREEZING! WHY DO WE KEEP THIS HOUSE SO DARN COLD?!

**Panel 6:** CRANK UP THE THERMOSTAT AND BUILD A FIRE, WILL YA? / I HAVE A BETTER IDEA. C'MERE.

**Panel 7:** OK, STEP OUTSIDE. / WHY? WHAT'S OUTSIDE?

**Panel 8:** IN A FEW MINUTES YOU CAN COME IN, AND THEN THE HOUSE WILL SEEM NICE AND WARM. / I'M TELLING THE NEWSPAPERS ABOUT YOU, DAD!

**Panel 9:** READ ME "HAMSTER HUEY AND THE GOOEY KABLOOIE." / OH, I DON'T WANT TO READ THAT AGAIN. LET'S READ SOMETHING DIFFERENT TONIGHT.

**Panel 10:** NO, I WANT TO HEAR "HAMSTER HUEY AND THE GOOEY KABLOOIE." / C'MON, CALVIN, I'VE READ THIS A THOUSAND TIMES.

**Panel 11:** READ IT AGAIN. PLEASE? *PLEASE?* / ALL RIGHT, ALL RIGHT.

**Panel 12:** YOU'LL DO THE SQUEAKY VOICES, THE GOOSHY SOUND EFFECTS, AND THE HAPPY HAMSTER HOP, WON'T YOU? / LOOK, CAN'T WE READ SOMETHING ELSE?

SHOVEL, SHOVEL, SHOVEL!

WHY CAN'T WE GET A SNOW BLOWER?? WE MUST BE THE ONLY FAMILY IN THE WORLD THAT STILL SHOVELS THE DRIVEWAY BY HAND! I'M FREEZING!

IT BUILDS CHARACTER. KEEP AT IT.

PRETTY CONVENIENT HOW EVERY TIME *I* BUILD CHARACTER, *HE* SAVES A COUPLE HUNDRED DOLLARS.

NEXT TIME WE GO DOWN, *I* GET TO STEER THE SLED.

*YOU*?! YOU STEER LIKE AN OLD LADY!

YEAH, WELL, I'M SICK OF GOING OVER AND THROUGH EVERY OBSTACLE ON THE HILL.

"EVERY OBSTACLE"?!? WE MISSED THE BRIAR PATCH, DIDN'T WE?!

BY GOING DOWN THE GULLY AND INTO THE STREAM, YES.

OH, YOU MAKE EVERYTHING SOUND SO TERRIBLE. YOU SHOULD BE GLAD WE'RE ALIVE.

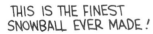

THIS IS THE FINEST SNOWBALL EVER MADE!

PAINSTAKINGLY HAND-CRAFTED INTO A PERFECT SPHERE FROM A SECRET MIXTURE OF SLUSH, ICE, DIRT, DEBRIS AND FINE POWDER SNOW, THIS *IS* THE ULTIMATE WINTER WEAPON!

YES, THIS MARVEL OF CRYSTALLINE ENGINEERING WI..

WHAP!

ANOTHER CASUALTY OF THE SEDUCTION OF ART.

WHAT DO YOU THINK IS THE BEST WAY TO GET WHAT YOU WANT? IS IT BETTER TO HOLD FAST AND NEVER BACK DOWN, OR TO COMPROMISE?

I SUPPOSE IT'S BEST TO HOLD FAST WHEN YOU CAN, AND COMPROMISE WHEN YOU NEED TO.

THAT'S A LOT MORE MATURE THAN I THINK I CARE TO BE.

I THINK THE SHORT ATTENTION SPAN OF TELEVISION IS GREAT.

AS FAR AS *I'M* CONCERNED, IF SOMETHING IS SO COMPLICATED THAT YOU CAN'T EXPLAIN IT IN 10 SECONDS, THEN IT'S PROBABLY NOT WORTH KNOWING ANYWAY.

MY TIME IS VALUABLE. I CAN'T GO THINKING ABOUT ONE SUBJECT FOR MINUTES ON END. I'M A BUSY MAN.

...WHO'S BEEN SITTING HERE FOR THREE HOURS.

... AT SIX THOUGHTS A MINUTE.

THERE'S SOMETHING MAGICAL ABOUT HAVING A FIRE.

THE CRACKLES AND SNAPS, THE WARM, FLICKERING LIGHT... EVERYTHING ALWAYS SEEMS SAFE AND COZY IF YOU'RE SITTING IN FRONT OF A FIRE.

AND IF YOU'VE GOT A HOT TIGER TUMMY TO LIE AGAINST.... *WELL!*

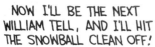

OK, LET'S SEE... IF THE WIND IS BLOWING NORTH-NORTHEAST AT 6 MPH, AND I THROW THE SNOWBALL DUE WEST AT 90 MPH WITH A SLIGHT TOP SPIN....

HA! SUSIE DIDN'T EVEN HEAR ME SNEAK UP!

NOW I'LL CREAM HER CRANIUM WITH A BARRAGE OF SNOWBALLS!

WHIZZZ

PIFF

PIFF

THESE DARN CROSS BREEZES! SHE DIDN'T EVEN NOTICE!

YOU'RE THE WORST SHOT IN THE WORLD, CALVIN! IF IT WASN'T FOR GRAVITY, YOU PROBABLY COULDN'T EVEN HIT THE GROUND!

SMACK!

I DID IT! I DID IT! JUST WHEN IT REALLY COUNTED, I DID IT! HA HA HA! RIGHT IN THE KISSER! HA HA!

BAD NEWS, MOM. I PROMISED MY SOUL TO THE DEVIL THIS AFTERNOON.

OH? THAT RECENTLY?

THE FEARLESS SPACEMAN SPIFF FINDS HIMSELF ON THE PLANET CLOSEST TO STAR X-351!

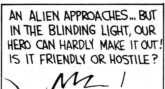

AN ALIEN APPROACHES... BUT IN THE BLINDING LIGHT, OUR HERO CAN HARDLY MAKE IT OUT! IS IT FRIENDLY OR HOSTILE?

WHAT ARE YOU DOING IN BED STILL?! GET READY FOR SCHOOL!

DEFINITELY HOSTILE.

THE SCHOOL BUS WILL BE HERE ANY MINUTE! GO! SCOOT!

SPACEMAN SPIFF, CAPTURED BY VICIOUS ZOGWARGS, IS ABOUT TO BE TRANSPORTED TO THE LABOR CAMP! OUR HERO HATCHES A BOLD PLAN!

AT THE LAST SECOND, SPIFF MAKES HIS BREAK! TAKING ADVANTAGE OF THE PLANET'S WEAKER GRAVITY, OUR HERO IS AWAY LIKE A SHOT.

THERE'S THE BUS... BUT WHY DON'T I SEE CALVIN?

SPIFF ESCAPES!

DID CALVIN GET ON THE BUS?

I DIDN'T SEE. ...WHY?

SOMEONE JUST DARTED BEHIND THAT TREE. SEE, THERE HE GOES AGAIN! ISN'T THAT CALVIN?

THE ZOGWARGS HAVE SPOTTED HIM! OUR HERO INFLATES THE EMERGENCY JET PACK HE KEEPS IN HIS POCKET, AND PREPARES FOR TAKEOFF!

YES, CAN I HAVE THE TOOL DEPARTMENT, PLEASE? THANK YOU.

HELLO? HOW MUCH ARE YOUR POWER CIRCULAR SAWS? I SEE. AND YOUR ELECTRIC DRILLS? UH-HUH. HOW BIG OF A BIT WILL THAT HOLD? REALLY? GREAT.

SO THE ASSIGNMENT IS PAGES TWO THROUGH FOUR? OK, THANKS SUSIE.

..SORRY ABOUT THAT. DO YOU CARRY ACETYLENE TORCHES? OK, RING IT ALL UP. THIS WILL BE ON MASTERCARD.

LOOK AT ALL THIS HOMEWORK I'M SUPPOSED TO DO!

I DON'T WANT TO DO THIS GARBAGE! I WANT TO GO PLAY OUTSIDE!

CHILDHOOD IS SHORT AND MATURITY IS FOREVER.

PEOPLE ARE ROTTEN.

WHEN I GROW UP, I'M GOING TO LIVE A MILLION MILES AWAY FROM EVERYONE!

HOW WILL YOU SURVIVE? WHAT WILL YOU EAT?

...WELL, MOM COULD COME BY TWICE A DAY TO COOK, I SUPPOSE.

THAT WOULD BE QUITE A COMMUTE.

GET A LOAD OF *THIS* DUMB ASSIGNMENT! I'M SUPPOSED TO WRITE ABOUT AN ADVENTURE I'VE HAD!

*I* HAVEN'T HAD ANY ADVENTURES! MY LIFE HAS BEEN ONE BIG BORE FROM THE BEGINNING!

HAVE I EVER BEEN ABDUCTED BY PIRATES? HAVE I EVER FACED DOWN A CHARGING RHINO? HAVE I EVER BEEN IN A SHOOT-OUT, OR ON A BOMBING RAID? **NO!** I NEVER GET TO HAVE ADVENTURES!

WHAT ABOUT THE TIME YOU BACKED THE CAR THROUGH THE GARAGE DOOR?

YOU CALL THAT AN ADVENTURE? I DIDN'T EVEN GET ON THE HIGHWAY.

WHEN DO YOU THINK WE'LL GET A THUNDER AND LIGHTNING STORM?

I DON'T KNOW. PROBABLY NOT UNTIL SPRING.

I THINK HE'S GOING TO MELT BEFORE WE CAN BRING HIM TO LIFE.

HEY, SUSIE, STAND ON THIS "X."

WHY?

NO REASON. JUST DO IT. I DARE YOU.

NO.

PLEASE? C'MON!

GET LOST.

THIS MAY NOT WORK OUT AS WELL AS I THOUGHT.

# CALVIN and HOBBES

by WATTERSON

# Calvin and Hobbes by WATTERSON

WHAT'S THIS?

A CALVIN DECOY. PRETTY GOOD, HUH?

NOW I CAN FIND OUT WHO MY ENEMIES ARE! I'LL HIDE BEHIND THAT TREE OVER THERE AND WATCH TO SEE WHO THROWS SNOWBALLS AT THE DECOY, THINKING IT'S ME!

YOUR ENEMIES MUST NOT BE VERY BRIGHT.

THAT'S WHY THEY'RE OUT TO GET ME. THEY CAN'T STAND MY GENIUS.

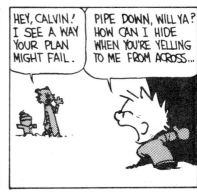

HEY, CALVIN! I SEE A WAY YOUR PLAN MIGHT FAIL.

PIPE DOWN, WILL YA? HOW CAN I HIDE WHEN YOU'RE YELLING TO ME FROM ACROSS...

SMACK!

SEE THERE? MY PLAN TO DISCOVER MY ENEMIES WAS A COMPLETE SUCCESS.

TOO BAD YOU TOOK OFF YOUR COAT AND HAT. YOU MUST BE SOAKED.

HERE WE ARE, POISED ON THE PRECIPICE OF "SUICIDE SLOPE." BELOW US LIE THE SKELETAL REMAINS OF HUNDREDS OF LITTLE SLED RIDERS.

SEARCHING FOR THAT ULTIMATE ADRENALINE RUSH, WE PREPARE TO HURL OURSELVES OVER THE BRINK! WHAT FATE AWAITS US?

READY?

NO.

LIFE AND DEATH HANG IN THE BALANCE! A FRACTION OF A SECOND AND ONE WRONG TURN ARE ALL THAT SEPARATE THEM!

THIS ISN'T HELPING.

DAD SAYS THE ANTICIPATION OF HAVING SOMETHING IS OFTEN MORE FUN THAN ACTUALLY HAVING IT.

I THINK HE'S CRAZY. I HATE WAITING FOR THINGS. I LIKE TO HAVE EVERYTHING IMMEDIATELY.

I CAN'T THINK OF *ANYTHING* I'D RATHER ANTICIPATE THAN HAVE RIGHT AWAY. CAN YOU?

DEATH COMES TO MIND.

I DON'T KNOW WHY I BOTHER TRYING TO HAVE A LITTLE DISCUSSION WITH YOU WHEN YOU'RE ALWAYS SO MORBID.

I WISH SNOW WAS DRY, SO THAT YOU DIDN'T GET ALL COLD AND WET WHEN YOU PLAYED IN IT.

...THEN AGAIN, IF SNOW WAS DRY, YOU COULDN'T PACK IT INTO SNOWBALLS. THAT WOULDN'T BE GOOD.

I WISH IT SNOWED IN SUMMER. WOULDN'T THAT BE FUN? ...WELL NO, ACTUALLY THAT WOULD MAKE IT HARD TO RUN WHEN YOU PLAY BASEBALL.

HECK, IT'S OK JUST THE WAY IT IS.

WE'RE GLAD YOU APPROVE.

40

YOU CAN ALWAYS TELL WHEN YOU GET TO *OUR* HOUSE.

I THINK OUR SNOW FORTS ARE TOO FAR APART.

POP!

NOW LET'S SEE IF MOM JUMPS OUT OF *HER* SKIN!

# CALVIN and HOBBES by WATTERSON

CLUMP

THE PTERANODON SPREADS HIS GIANT WINGS, AND..

LOOK AT THIS, HOBBES! I COULD ORDER AN OFFICIAL CHOCOLATE FROSTED SUGAR BOMBS BEANIE!

SEE, IT HAS A BATTERY-POWERED PROPELLER ON TOP AND A BIG STAR ON THE FRONT! ISN'T THAT NEAT?

YOU HAVE TO SEND IN FOUR BOX "PROOF OF PURCHASE SEALS" TO GET IT, IT SAYS.

WELL, DON'T JUST STAND THERE, OR THIS'LL TAKE FOREVER.

UGH. THIS STUFF ALWAYS MAKES MY HEART SKIP.

BLECHH. I FEEL SICK.

OH, C'MON, THAT'S ONLY YOUR SECOND BOWL OF CEREAL.

THIS STUFF IS PURE SUGAR.

BUT IT'S *FORTIFIED* WITH EIGHT ESSENTIAL VITAMINS, SO IT'S GOOD FOR YOU.

GIVE ME A BREAK. THIS IS LIKE EATING A BOWL OF MILK DUDS.

LOOK, IT SAYS RIGHT ON THE BOX, "PART OF A WHOLESOME, NUTRITIOUS, BALANCED BREAKFAST."

AND THEY SHOW A GUY EATING FIVE GRAPEFRUITS, A DOZEN BRAN MUFFINS...

YOU KNOW WHY YOU SHAKE LIKE THAT? VITAMIN DEFICIENCY, I'LL BET.

'MORNING, DAD! HOW'S YOUR BREAKFAST?

FINE.

OATMEAL, HUH? A BOWL OF PASTY, BLAND, COLORLESS SLUDGE.

YES. WHY DON'T YOU GO DESCRIBE YOUR *OWN* FOOD SOMEWHERE ELSE?

I'LL BET YOU'D RATHER HAVE A BOWL OF TASTY, LIP-SMACKING, CRUNCHY-ON-THE-OUTSIDE, CHEWY-ON-THE-INSIDE, CHOCOLATE FROSTED SUGAR BOMBS! CAN I POUR YOU SOME?

NO, THANKS. I'M TRYING TO REACH MIDDLE AGE.

WHAT ARE *YOU* HAVING, MOM? BORING OLD TOAST AND TEA?

*YOU* WANT THE BEANIE, *YOU* EAT THE CEREAL, CALVIN.

1½ BOXES TO GO, AND I'LL HAVE ENOUGH "PROOF OF PURCHASE SEALS" TO ORDER THE PROPELLER BEANIE THEY OFFER.

1⅓ BOXES TO GO.

MAN, I'M *EARNING* THIS.

HOBBES, I DID IT! I ATE ENOUGH BOXES OF CEREAL TO GET ALL THE PROOF OF PURCHASE SEALS I NEED!

NOW I CAN ORDER MY BEANIE! OH, BOY! I CAN'T WAIT TO GET IT! I'LL BE SO COOL!

NOT FOR OVER A MONTH. IT SAYS TO ALLOW SIX WEEKS FOR DELIVERY.

SIX WEEKS ?!?

I'LL BE *OLD* THEN!

AND I'M SURE YOUR BEANIE WILL BE THE TALK OF THE REST HOME.

MOM! MOM! DID MY BEANIE COME IN THE MAIL?

ARE YOU KIDDING? I JUST MAILED YOUR ORDER THIS MORNING.

I'M NEVER GOING TO MAKE IT SIX WEEKS.

I CAN'T BELIEVE THIS. EVERY DAY I GET ALL MY HOPES UP, THINKING MY BEANIE WILL COME... AND THEN IT DOESN'T.

AND FOR EACH DAY THAT GOES BY, I FIGURE THE ODDS ARE BETTER THAT IT WILL COME THE *NEXT* DAY, SO MY HOPES GET HIGHER AND HIGHER BEFORE THEY FALL. IT'S AWFUL.

BUT I'VE BEEN DISAPPOINTED SO OFTEN NOW, I'M FINALLY GETTING NUMB TO IT.

MAYBE THE MAILMAN MADE A SECOND TRIP TODAY AND DELIVERED IT IN THE LAST FIVE MINUTES.

WOW! I NEVER THOUGHT OF THAT! C'MON!

HE'S NOT NUMB.

THE LONGER YOU WAIT FOR THE MAIL, THE LESS THERE IS IN IT.

I'M HOME. I DIDN'T GET MY PROPELLER BEANIE TODAY, DID I?

AS A MATTER OF FACT, YOU DID!

IT'S HERE!

HA HA! IT TOOK WEEKS AND WEEKS OF WAITING, BUT AT LONG LAST IT'S HERE! NOW I FINALLY, *FINALLY* GET TO PUT IT ON!

"SOME ASSEMBLY REQUIRED. BATTERIES NOT INCLUDED."

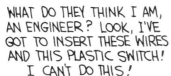

# CALVIN and HOBBES by WATTERSON

I CAN NEVER ENJOY SUNDAYS, BECAUSE IN THE BACK OF MY MIND I ALWAYS KNOW I'VE GOT TO GO TO SCHOOL THE NEXT DAY.

IT'S LIKE TRYING TO ENJOY YOUR LAST MEAL BEFORE THE EXECUTION.

A PENNY FOR YOUR THOUGHTS.

SORRY. *MY* THOUGHTS ARE A BUCK APIECE.

A DOLLAR?! THAT'S OUTRAGEOUS! YOUR THOUGHTS AREN'T WORTH THAT!

*THIS* ONE IS! AT A DOLLAR, IT'S THE BARGAIN OF A LIFETIME.

I WOULDN'T PAY A NICKEL FOR ANY THOUGHT YOU'VE EVER HAD IN YOUR WHOLE FLEA-RIDDEN EXISTENCE!

THAT LITTLE REMARK JUST MADE THE PRICE *TEN* DOLLARS!

*TEN??* YOU CAN'T EXTORT ME! *KEEP* YOUR STUPID THOUGHT!

IF YOU KNEW WHAT IT WAS, YOU'D *BEG* TO PAY TEN BUCKS FOR IT.

C'MON, JUST TELL ME WHAT IT IS, WILL YOU?

NOTHING DOING, PAL.

OK, OK! I'LL GIVE YOU 25 CENTS. THAT'S ALL I HAVE.

LET'S SEE IT.

*HERE!* 25 CENTS! NOW WHAT'S THIS BIG, EXPENSIVE THOUGHT OF YOURS?!

"A FOOL AND HIS MONEY ARE SOON PAR..."

52

PHOOEY. NO BUGS IN THE BUS WINDOW.

I CAN'T BELIEVE YOU'RE DOING THIS.

CHOOL DISTRI

HEY, ASK THAT KID IF HE'S GOT ANY BUGS IN *HIS* WINDOW.

CALVIN, THERE IS NO WAY YOU'RE GOING TO COMPLETE AN INSECT COLLECTION ON THE WAY TO SCHOOL! FORGET IT!

SIGHHH... WELL, MAYBE YOU'RE RIGHT.

HOW MUCH DO YOU WANT FOR *YOUR* COLLECTION? I'LL GIVE YOU A QUARTER...OR HERE, 30 CENTS.

I SPENT A MONTH ON THIS!

HEY, HERE'S A WORM! WORMS ARE BUGS, AREN'T THEY?

EWW GROSS, CALVIN! THAT'S BEEN FLOATING IN A PUDDLE FOR DAYS.

CLASS DOESN'T START FOR 10 MINUTES. IF I CAN CATCH FIVE BUGS A MINUTE, I'LL GET AN "A" ON MY COLLECTION. SEE, I'M OFF TO A GOOD START.

FIVE BUGS A MINUTE?! YOU'RE OUT OF YOUR MIND.

HERE'S ANOTHER ALREADY.

THAT'S A LITTLE BALL OF LINT!

LIKE I'M SURE THE TEACHER'S GOING TO LOOK **REAL CLOSE** AT EVERY HAIRY BUG IN 30 KIDS' COLLECTIONS!

RINNGGGG

THERE'S THE BELL. WE'VE GOT TO GO TO CLASS.

RATS. I DIDN'T GET 50 BUGS YET.

WHAT DO YOU HAVE?

ONE DROWNED WORM, A PIECE OF FUZZY LINT THAT *LOOKS* LIKE A BUG, A LIVE ANT, AND A SMASHED FLY.

WELL, IF YOU LABEL THEM SCIENTIFICALLY IN THE NEXT 30 SECONDS, MAYBE YOU'LL GET AN "F+."

WE'VE GOT TO *LABEL* THESE *TOO*?!? I WAS JUST GOING TO PUT THEM ALL IN AN ENVELOPE.

ACTUALLY, I DON'T THINK THERE'S ANY WAY YOU'LL GET AN "F+."

FOR ALL THIS WORK, I'D BETTER AT LEAST GET A "D."

HOW DID YOU MOUNT YOUR INSECTS, SUSIE?

IN THIS BOX WITH PINS.

HMM... I DON'T HAVE A BOX OR PINS. I GUESS I'LL JUST STICK MY BUGS ON NOTEBOOK PAPER.

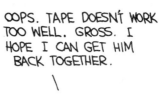

OOPS. TAPE DOESN'T WORK TOO WELL. GROSS. I HOPE I CAN GET HIM BACK TOGETHER.

CAN I BORROW YOUR PASTE?

THE WAY YOU'RE GOING, MAYBE YOU'D PREFER A STAPLER.

PSST...SUSIE! HELP ME THINK UP SCIENTIFIC NAMES OF MY BUGS WHILE THE TEACHER'S NOT LOOKING.

SHHH! WE'RE NOT SUPPOSED TO TALK IN CLASS. DO IT YOURSELF.

HAVING A PLEASANT CONVERSATION, MISS DERKINS?

EEEP!

PERHAPS YOU'D LIKE TO SIT UP FRONT, SO YOU WON'T DISTRACT CALVIN ANYMORE.

OH, I *TRIED* TO GET HER TO BE QUIET, BUT YOU KNOW HOW GIRLS ARE.

OOOOH, THAT ROTTEN CALVIN! I HATE HIM! I HATE HIM!

*HE'S* THE ONE WHO DIDN'T DO THE ASSIGNMENT! *HE'S* THE ONE WHO WAS TALKING IN CLASS! *HE'S* THE ONE WHO SHOULD BE SITTING HERE AT THE FRONT OF THE ROOM, NOT *ME!*

*I* WASN'T DOING ANYTHING WRONG, BUT *I'M* THE ONE WHO GOT IN TROUBLE! I SURE HOPE CALVIN FEELS TERRIBLE ABOUT THIS!

Hey SUSiE, HOW'S tHE VIEW WaY UP tHERE? Ha! Ha! CaLViN

P.S. tRY to StEaL a CHaLkBoaRD ERaSER FoR ME.

HERE COMES SUSIE, BACK FROM THE PRINCIPAL'S OFFICE. BOY, DOES SHE LOOK PALE. I WONDER WHAT HAPPENED. SHE'S TALKING TO THE TEACHER NOW.

PSST! SUSIE, WHAT DID THEY DO TO YOU? DID YOU GET EXPELLED? YOU DIDN'T SNITCH ON *ME*, DID YOU?

YOU *DID* SNITCH! YOU'RE A *STOOLIE!* A CANARY!

YOU'RE GOING UP THE RIVER, CALVIN.

CALVIN, WILL YOU COME HERE, PLEASE?

SO *FIRST* I GOT IN TROUBLE FOR NOT PAYING ATTENTION IN CLASS AND FOR TURNING IN A LAST-MINUTE INSECT COLLECTION, WHICH I GOT A "D-MINUS-MINUS" ON.

*THEN* I GOT IN TROUBLE FOR GETTING *SUSIE* IN TROUBLE WHEN I WANTED HER TO HELP ME FUDGE THE PROJECT.

*THEN* I GOT IN TROUBLE WHEN I TOLD MOM, AND *THEN* I GOT IN TROUBLE *AGAIN* WHEN *SHE* TOLD *DAD!* I'VE BEEN IN HOT WATER EVER SINCE I GOT UP!

WOW. I'LL BET ALL THIS MAKES YOU GET YOUR BOOK REPORT FINISHED RIGHT ON TIME.

MY WHAT?

ONE OF NATURE'S MOST PECULIAR-LOOKING CREATURES, THE GIRAFFE IS UNIQUELY SUITED TO ITS ENVIRONMENT.

HIS TREMENDOUS HEIGHT ENABLES HIM TO MUNCH ON THE SUCCULENT MORSELS MOST DIFFICULT TO REACH.

# CALVIN and HOBBES

by WATTERSON

SIGHHHHH...

WHAP

SIGHHHHH...

HOW COME **YOU** ALWAYS READ ME MY BEDTIME STORY AND NOT MOM?

BECAUSE READING THE BEDTIME STORY IS THE **DAD'S** JOB.

AND IT APPEARS TO BE THE **ONLY** "DAD'S JOB" AROUND HERE!

LEFT THE DISHES FOR MOM AGAIN, HUH?

TONIGHT'S STORY IS CALLED, "WHY PRINCE CHARMING STAYED SINGLE."

PRINCE **WHAT**?

I'VE BEEN THINKING. SUPPOSE I GROW UP TO BE ONE OF THE WORLD'S GREATEST MEN OF ALL TIME. SUPPOSE MY NAME WILL BE AN INSPIRATION TO HUMANITY FOR EONS TO COME!

WHAT WILL THE HISTORY BOOKS SAY? THEY'LL SAY, "MUCH OF HIS CHILDHOOD WAS SPENT UNWILLINGLY IN THE BATHTUB."

WHAT AN INDIGNITY THIS BATH IS! IS THIS SITUATION WORTHY OF ONE OF THE GREATEST MEN OF ALL TIME?!?

MY LIKELY HISTORICAL SIGNIFICANCE IS A TERRIBLE BURDEN.

WOULD YOU RATHER THEY SAID YOUR CHILDHOOD WAS DIRTY AND SMELLY?

NNNGKGKK

HOCCHHHH

PTOOEY!

BOY, THEY SURE GO FARTHER WHEN YOU MAKE 'EM RIGHT!

LET'S MAKE UP A **NEW** CONTEST, OK?

# CALVIN and HOBBES

by WATTERSON

THREE... TWO..., ONE...

**LIGHT SPEED!**

BLASTING ACROSS THE GALAXY IN HYPER LIGHT DRIVE, IT'S *SPACEMAN SPIFF*, INTERPLANETARY EXPLORER EXTRAORDIN...

SINCE CALVIN SEEMS TO BE ENJOYING THE LESSON, LET'S HAVE HIM DEMONSTRATE THE NEXT PROBLEM.

*ZOUNDS!* A ZOK DEATH SLOOP APPEARS OUT OF NOWHERE AND FRIES SPIFF'S STABILIZERS!

OUR HERO HURLS OUT OF CONTROL TOWARD HIS IMMINENT DOOM!

THE SITUATION IS DESPERATE! THIS COULD BE THE END! WHAT CAN OUR HERO DO??

HIS MIND RACING FURIOUSLY, SPIFF SPRINGS INTO ACTION! HE DOWNSHIFTS HIS SPACECRAFT AND...

... STALLS.

**RINGG!**

OH, DARN, OUT OF TIME.

ONCE AGAIN SPACEMAN SPIFF BEATS ALL ODDS TO SAVE THE DAY!

# CALVIN and HOBBES
by WATTERSON

I'M HOME!

YAHHH

SLAM!

WHAT A CHUMP!

KNOCK KNOCK

FORGET IT, YOU MORON! I'M NOT OPENING THE DOOR! YOU CAN JUST STAY OUT THERE ALL NIGHT!

OH, I CAN'T *WAIT* TO HEAR *THIS* ONE EXPLAINED.

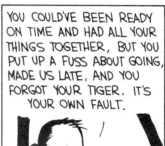

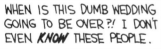

OH MY GOSH!! SOMEBODY BROKE INTO OUR HOUSE!!

I'LL CALL THE POLICE!

WHERE'S HOBBES?

I CAN'T BELIEVE THIS IS HAPPENING! LOOK AT THIS ROOM!

HOBBES! OH, I *KNEW* WE SHOULDN'T HAVE LEFT HIM HERE!

MOM, I CAN'T FIND HOBBES! HELP ME FIND HIM! WHAT IF I... WHAT IF THEY...

IT'S OK, CALVIN. CALM DOWN. I'M SURE HOBBES IS HERE SOME-WHERE.

I DON'T THINK ANYONE WOULD STEAL A STUFFED TIGER. C'MON, LET'S GO LOOK.

BUT HOBBES IS SO *TRUSTING*..

SNIFF

THE POLICE SAY THEY'LL SEND SOMEONE OVER. HAVE YOU FIGURED OUT WHAT ALL IS MISSING?

NO, WE'RE LOOKING FOR HOBBES. CALVIN'S ALMOST HYSTERICAL.

I FEEL A LITTLE HYSTER-ICAL MYSELF.

OOH...I HOPE THE POLICE GET HERE QUICK. I'M SCARED.

THIS IS ONE OF THOSE THINGS YOU ALWAYS FIGURE WILL HAPPEN TO SOMEONE ELSE.

...UNFORTUNATELY, WE'RE *ALL* "SOMEONE ELSE" TO SOMEONE ELSE.

HOBBES? HOBBES? WHERE ARE YOU ??

I *TOLD* MOM AND DAD WE LEFT HOBBES BEHIND.... I *TRIED* TO GET THEM TO TURN AROUND AND COME BACK .... AND *NOW* LOOK, HOBBES WAS ALL ALONE WHEN OUR HOUSE WAS BROKEN INTO!

MOM SAYS HOBBES WOULDN'T HAVE BEEN STOLEN BECAUSE HE'S NOT VALUABLE.

...(SNIFF) WELL, *I* THINK HE'S VALUABLE.

HOBBES? ARE YOU DOWN HERE? YOU'VE GOT TO BE *SOME*WHERE!

HERE HE IS, CALVIN! I FOUND HOBBES!

YOU *FOUND* HIM! IS HE OK?? HE'S NOT HURT, IS HE?

HE'S FINE. HE WAS UNDER THE BED COVERS.

HOBBES, I'M SO GLAD TO SEE YOU!! YOU'RE SAFE AND SOUND! (SNIFF) AND NOW I AM, TOO!

IT LOOKS LIKE WE'RE A WHOLE FAMILY AGAIN.

SUCH AS IT IS, YES.

...AND THE TELEVISION'S GONE, TOO.

DO YOU HAPPEN TO HAVE THE SERIAL NUMBER?

I'LL BET THE BURGLARS GOT SCARED OFF WHEN THEY SAW THERE WAS A TIGER IN THE HOUSE! HOBBES WAS HERE THE WHOLE TIME!

CALVIN, NOT NOW, OK? I'M BUSY.

NOBODY STICKS AROUND LONG WHEN HE SEES A TIGER, THAT'S FOR SURE! MANDIBLES OF DEATH, THAT'S WHAT HOBBES HAS!

RIGHT. WHY DON'T YOU GO TELL YOUR MOM?

MAYBE HOBBES SHOULD LOOK AT SOME MUG SHOTS. CAN WE GO TO THE STATION AND IDENTIFY SUSPECTS? HUH, CAN WE?

DEAR!

I SURE MEET THE WEIRDOS IN THIS JOB..

I'VE SWEPT UP MOST OF THE GLASS FROM THE WINDOW.

OK, I'LL GET SOMETHING TO COVER UP THE HOLE.

DO YOU THINK IT'S SAFE TO STAY HERE TONIGHT? SUPPOSE THE BURGLARS COME BACK!

THE POLICE SAID THEY'D DRIVE BY, AND WE'LL LEAVE LOTS OF LIGHTS ON.

UGH, IT'S SO CREEPY KNOWING THESE GOONS HAVE BEEN IN OUR HOUSE. I DON'T FEEL SAFE AT ALL.

I KNOW. AND THIS MUST *REALLY* BE SCARY FOR A LITTLE KID LIKE CALVIN.

GOSH, I CAN'T WAIT TO TELL EVERYONE AT SCHOOL HOW OUR HOUSE GOT ROBBED!

BE SURE TO SAY WHO SCARED THE BURGLARS AWAY AFTER THEY TOOK THE TV AND JEWELRY.

IS CALVIN ASLEEP?

YES, HE'S SNUGGLED UP WITH HOBBES.

BOY, I DON'T KNOW HOW *I'M* EVER GOING TO SLEEP.

ME NEITHER. I CAN'T GET OVER WHAT'S HAPPENED.

THE IDEA OF SOME CRAZY STRANGER GOING THROUGH OUR HOUSE... *BRRRR!!* I WISH *I* HAD A BIG STUFFED ANIMAL TO FEEL SAFE WITH.

I GUESS YOU'LL HAVE TO DO.

SO WHAT DO *I* GET TO SNUGGLE? HOW COME *I'M* THE GROWN-UP??

THIS IS GOING TO BE A LONG NIGHT.

MY HEART JUMPS AT THE SLIGHTEST SOUND. IT'S ALMOST 2, AND I'M WIDE AWAKE.

WHEN SOMEONE BREAKS INTO YOUR HOME, IT SHATTERS YOUR LAST ILLUSION OF SECURITY. IF YOU'RE NOT SAFE IN YOUR OWN HOME, YOU'RE NOT SAFE ANYWHERE.

A MAN'S HOME IS HIS CASTLE, BUT IT SHOULDN'T HAVE TO BE A FORTRESS.

ARE YOU STILL AWAKE TOO?

MM-HMM. I WAS THINKING.

IT'S FUNNY... WHEN I WAS A KID, I THOUGHT GROWN-UPS NEVER WORRIED ABOUT ANYTHING. I TRUSTED MY PARENTS TO TAKE CARE OF EVERYTHING, AND IT NEVER OCCURRED TO ME THAT THEY MIGHT NOT KNOW HOW.

I FIGURED THAT ONCE YOU GREW UP, YOU AUTOMATICALLY KNEW WHAT TO DO IN ANY GIVEN SCENARIO.

I DON'T THINK I'D HAVE BEEN IN SUCH A HURRY TO REACH ADULTHOOD IF I'D KNOWN THE WHOLE THING WAS GOING TO BE AD-LIBBED.

WELL, AT LEAST WE WEREN'T HOME WHEN OUR HOUSE WAS BROKEN INTO. NO ONE WAS HURT. WE'RE ALL TOGETHER AND OK.

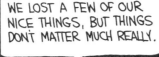

WE LOST A FEW OF OUR NICE THINGS, BUT THINGS DON'T MATTER MUCH REALLY.

IT'S HARD TO BELIEVE HOW OFTEN WE FORGET THAT.

CAN I BE EXCUSED NOW?

YOU DIDN'T FINISH YOUR DINNER.

WELL, I DIDN'T LIKE IT VERY MUCH, AND THERE'S THIS TV SHOW I WANT TO WATCH, SO...

OUR TV WAS STOLEN, REMEMBER?

GOSH, I GUESS I'LL EAT MY ASPARAGUS, DO MY HOMEWORK, AND GO STRAIGHT TO BED, THEN.

AND WE'RE SO PROUD OF HOW YOU HANDLE ADVERSITY.

THIS IS WHERE OUR TELEVISION USED TO BE.

BUT WE DON'T HAVE A TV ANYMORE. NOW WE HAVE A BLANK WALL TO WATCH.

SO HERE I AM, NOT BEING ENTERTAINED.

A POINTLESS EXISTENCE, HUH?

I MEAN, THE WALL IS EVEN PLAIN OLD *WHITE!*

# CALViN and HObbEs

by WATTERSN

I CAN'T SLEEP.

I THINK NIGHTTIME IS DARK SO YOU CAN IMAGINE YOUR FEARS WITH LESS DISTRACTION.

AT NIGHTTIME, THE WORLD ALWAYS SEEMS SO BIG AND SCARY, AND I ALWAYS SEEM SO SMALL.

I WISH I COULD FALL ASLEEP, SO IT WOULD BE MORNING.

SIGHHHHH..

LOOK AT HOBBES. *HE'S* ASLEEP.

Z

HEH HEH... HE SURE LOOKS FUNNY WHEN HE SLEEPS. TIGERS CLOSE THEIR EYES SO TIGHT. I WONDER WHAT HE'S DREAMING ABOUT.

GOOD OL' HOBBES. WHAT A FRIEND.

Z

THINGS ARE NEVER QUITE AS SCARY WHEN YOU'VE GOT A BEST FRIEND.

Z

Z

Z       Z

GOOD NEWS, HOBBES! I'M STARTING A SECRET CLUB, AND YOU CAN BE IN IT!

OH, BOY!

IT'LL BE GREAT! WE'LL THINK OF SECRET NAMES FOR OURSELVES, SECRET CODES FOR OUR SECRET CORRESPONDENCE, A SECRET HANDSHAKE, ...

WE'LL HAVE A SECRET CLUB-HOUSE WITH A SECRET KNOCK TO GET IN, AND WE'LL DO BIG, SECRETIVE THINGS!

WHY ALL THE SECRECY?

PEOPLE PAY MORE ATTENTION TO YOU WHEN THEY THINK YOU'RE UP TO SOMETHING.

OK, THE FIRST THING WE NEED IS A NAME FOR OUR SECRET CLUB.

LET'S CALL IT "THE HOBBES FAN CLUB"!

THE HOBBES FAN CLUB?! GIVE ME A BREAK! I'M SURE!!

THIS IS A TOP-SECRET SOCIETY! THE NAME SHOULD BE SOMETHING *MYSTERIOUS!* SOMETHING VAGUELY OMINOUS AND CHILLING!

SOMETHING LIKE, "THE SINISTER ICY BLACK HAND OF DEATH CLUB"!

I STILL LIKE MY IDEA BETTER.

I'VE GOT IT! WE'LL CALL OUR CLUB G.R.O.S.S. - *GET RID OF SLIMY GIRLS!* THAT WAY, SUSIE DERKINS CAN'T JOIN!

IS SHE SLIMY?

*ALL* GIRLS ARE SLIMY. NOW THE FIRST ORDER OF BUSINESS IS TO ELECT OFFICERS.

I GET TO BE PRESIDENT! I GET TO BE PRESIDENT!

OH, NO YOU DON'T! THIS WHOLE CLUB WAS *MY* IDEA, SO *I* GET TO BE PRESIDENT.

OK, THEN I GET TO BE KING AND TYRANT.

HEY, NO! *THAT'S* WHAT *I* WANT TO BE! YOU CAN BE PRESIDENT!

HI, CALVIN! WHAT ARE YOU DOING, MAKING PAPER HATS? CAN I MAKE ONE, TOO?

DON'T BE RIDICULOUS. THIS IS THE OFFICIAL CHAPEAU OF OUR TOP-SECRET CLUB, G.R.O.S.S. — GET RID OF SLIMY GIRLS!

"SLIMY GIRLS"?!

I KNOW THAT'S REDUNDANT, BUT OTHERWISE IT DOESN'T SPELL ANYTHING. NOW GO AWAY.

GIRLS AREN'T SLIMY!

DON'T GET GUNK ON ME. I TOOK A BATH LAST SATURDAY AND I'M ALL CLEAN.

I CAN'T BELIEVE YOU STARTED A SECRET CLUB JUST TO EXCLUDE GIRLS! THERE'S NOTHING WRONG WITH GIRLS!

SEE, HOBBES? GIRLS ARE SO EMOTIONAL.

YOU'RE THE MEANEST, MOST ROTTEN LITTLE KID I KNOW! WELL, FINE! PLAY WITH YOUR STUFFED TIGER! SEE WHAT I CARE! I DON'T WANT TO PLAY WITH A STINKER LIKE YOU ANYWAY!!

WOW, WHAT A GREAT CLUB!

OK, WE'VE GOT A SIGN FOR OUR SECRET CLUB, SO NOW WE NEED TO FIND A SECRET MEETING PLACE.

I KNOW! WE CAN SET UP A CARD TABLE IN THE GARAGE! THAT WOULD BE PERFECT FOR DRAWING UP MAPS AND STUFF!

HMM, THERE'S NOT MUCH ROOM WITH THE CAR HERE. LET'S PUSH IT INTO THE DRIVE.

SHOULDN'T YOU ASK YOUR MOM TO MOVE IT INSTEAD?

NAHH. SHE WON'T CARE IF WE PUSH IT OUT. C'MON.

IN THE PAST, YOU'VE BEEN A REMARKABLY POOR JUDGE OF WHAT YOUR MOM CARES ABOUT.

WHAT'S GOING ON, I WONDER. WHY ARE ALL THOSE CARS SLOWING DOWN AS THEY GO BY?

GOSH, DID SOMEONE HAVE AN ACCIDENT? IT LOOKS LIKE THERE'S A CAR IN THE DITCH! ...BUT I DON'T SEE ANYONE BY IT.

AND HOW ON EARTH DID THEY GO IN STRAIGHT BACKWARD? TO DO THAT, THE CAR WOULD'VE HAD TO COME...

...RIGHT...OUT...OUR... DRIVEWAY!

WELL, MOM'S SURE TO HAVE FOUND THE CAR BY NOW AND GUESSED WHAT WE DID.

NOW I KNOW WHAT THEY MEAN WHEN THEY SAY YOU CAN'T GO HOME AGAIN.

WHAT'S THAT SOUND?

I DON'T HEAR ANYTHING.

THERE! SOMETHING IS CRASHING THROUGH THE BRUSH!

IT SOUNDS BIG! MAYBE IT'S A BEAR!

THERE ARE *BEARS* OUT HERE??

CLIMB THE TREE! CLIMB THE TREE!

IF YOU ASK *ME*, TIGERS ARE THE ONLY FEROCIOUS ANIMALS THE WORLD REALLY NEEDS.

"BOY, 6, KILLED BY BEAR! PARENTS SAVED THE TROUBLE."

DO YOU THINK WE'RE SAFE? SHOULD WE CLIMB HIGHER?

IT'S HARD TO SAY WITH BEARS.

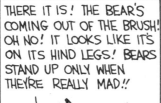

THERE IT IS! THE BEAR'S COMING OUT OF THE BRUSH! OH NO! IT LOOKS LIKE IT'S ON ITS HIND LEGS! BEARS STAND UP ONLY WHEN THEY'RE REALLY MAD!!

WAIT, THAT'S NOT A BEAR. THAT'S YOUR MOM!

AAUGHH! EVEN WORSE! CLIMB HIGHER! CLIMB HIGHER!

THERE YOU ARE. COME DOWN SO I CAN TALK TO YOU.

NO. YOU'LL KILL US. WE'RE RUNNING AWAY.

I'M NOT GOING TO KILL YOU. I JUST WANT TO FIND OUT WHAT HAPPENED. ARE YOU OK? WAS ANYONE HURT?

NO ONE WAS HURT. WE WERE PUSHING THE CAR INTO THE DRIVE AND IT KEPT ROLLING.

THE CAR DIDN'T HIT ANYTHING?

IT JUST WENT ACROSS THE ROAD AND INTO THE DITCH. THAT'S WHEN WE TOOK OFF.

WELL, THE TOW TRUCK PULLED IT OUT, AND THERE'S NO DAMAGE, SO YOU CAN COME HOME NOW.

FIRST LET'S HEAR YOU SAY YOU LOVE ME.

BOY, HOBBES, ISN'T IT FUNNY HOW THINGS SOMETIMES WORK OUT? MOM AND DAD SAW RIGHT AWAY THAT WHAT HAPPENED TO THE CAR WAS AN ACCIDENT.

THEY WERE SO RELIEVED NO ONE GOT HURT THAT ALL WE GOT WAS A LECTURE ON SAFETY AND ASKING PERMISSION. THEY DIDN'T EVEN RAISE THEIR VOICES.

PARENTS ARE SURE INSCRUTABLE, HUH? SEND THEIR CAR OVER A DITCH AND YOU DON'T EVEN GET YELLED AT.

... BUT TRY KEEPING LIVE WORMS IN YOUR DAD'S...

LET'S NOT TALK ABOUT THAT, OK?!

# Calvin and Hobbes

by WATTERSON

MILD-MANNERED CALVIN IS STUCK INSIDE DOING MATH PROBLEMS ON A BEAUTIFUL SUNDAY.

NO ONE IS WATCHING! HE DASHES INTO HIS CLOSET! *THIS* IS A JOB FOR...

STUPENDOUS MAN!

DEFENDER OF FREEDOM! ADVOCATE OF LIBERTY!

A BRIGHT CRIMSON STREAK BLASTS UP THROUGH THE ATMOSPHERE, AND THEN TURNS BACK TOWARD EARTH!

GAINING STUPENDOUS MOMENTUM, *STUPENDOUS MAN* STRIKES THE GROUND AT AN ACUTE ANGLE WITH STUPENDOUS FORCE!

THE EARTH SLOWLY STOPS ROTATING... AND BEGINS TO TURN IN THE OPPOSITE DIRECTION!

PUSHING WITH ALL HIS MIGHT, *STUPENDOUS MAN* TURNS THE PLANET ALL THE WAY AROUND BACKWARD! THE SUN SETS IN THE EAST AND RISES IN THE WEST! SOON IT'S 10 A.M. THE PREVIOUS DAY!

WHAT ARE YOU DOING OUTSIDE? DID YOU FINISH YOUR HOMEWORK ALREADY?

IT'S SATURDAY! I DON'T NEED TO DO IT UNTIL TOMORROW... *THANKS TO STUPENDOUS MAN!*

HERE'S THE LATEST POLL OF HOUSEHOLD 6-YEAR-OLDS, DAD.

AN OVERWHELMING MAJORITY EXPRESS AMAZEMENT AT HOW LITTLE YOU'VE ACCOMPLISHED AS DAD SO FAR. THE IMPRESSION IS THAT YOU'RE AVOIDING ALL THE HARD DECISIONS THAT NEED TO BE MADE.

IN FACT, NONE OF THOSE POLLED COULD NAME A SINGLE INSTANCE OF TRUE PATERNAL LEADERSHIP.

HOW ABOUT IF I LEAD YOU UPSTAIRS TO YOUR BED?

HA HA. IF WE CAN BE SERIOUS FOR A MOMENT, I HAVE SOME INNOVATIVE IDEAS ABOUT MY ALLOWANCE.

LOOK AT ALL THESE ANTS.

THEY'RE ALL RUNNING LIKE MAD, WORKING TIRELESSLY ALL DAY, NEVER STOPPING, NEVER RESTING.

AND FOR WHAT? TO BUILD A TINY LITTLE HILL OF SAND THAT COULD BE WIPED OUT AT ANY MOMENT! ALL THEIR WORK COULD BE FOR NOTHING, AND YET THEY KEEP ON BUILDING. THEY NEVER GIVE UP!

I SUPPOSE THERE'S A LESSON IN THAT.

YEAH ... ANTS ARE MORONS. LET'S SEE WHAT'S ON TV.

BOY, WHAT A GROUCH.

84

**Calvin and Hobbes** by WATTERSON

BLIPP    BLOOP

SPLOPP    BLIBB

LET'S FACE IT, WE'RE AESTHETES.

HERE COMES SUSIE. JUST IGNORE HER.

HI, CALVIN. CAN I PLAY WITH YOU AND YOUR TIGER?

HOBBES AND I ARE *NOT* PLAYING. WE'RE DOING BIG IMPORTANT THINGS, AND WE DON'T NEED YOU TO MESS THEM UP.

IT DOESN'T LOOK TO *ME* LIKE YOU'RE DOING ANYTHING SO IMPORTANT.

WELL WE ARE, SO GO AWAY. WE'VE WASTED TOO MUCH TIME TALKING TO YOU ALREADY.

YOU'RE JUST PLAYING IN THE MUD!

THAT'S JUST WHAT IT *LOOKS* LIKE TO IGNORANT GIRLS LIKE YOU! GET LOST!

ALL RIGHT, YOU LITTLE CREEP! I DON'T NEED YOU! I'VE GOT BETTER THINGS TO DO THAN SIT IN THE MUD LIKE A PIG!

A PIG?! BY GOLLY, I'LL SHOW *YOU*!

DON'T BEND OVER! YOUR CURLY PINK TAIL SHOWS! OINK! OINK! OINK! OINK!

EAT SOME MUD, SUSIE!

HA HA! YOU MISSED! OINK! OINK! OINK!

AHHH, SPRING! THAT MAGICAL TIME OF YEAR WHEN A YOUNG MAN'S FANCY TURNS TO LOVE!

SHUT UP.

CLEANING MY ROOM WILL GO A LOT FASTER IF WE *BOTH* WORK, RIGHT?

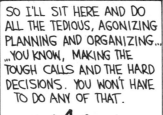

SO I'LL SIT HERE AND DO ALL THE TEDIOUS, AGONIZING PLANNING AND ORGANIZING... ...YOU KNOW, MAKING THE TOUGH CALLS AND THE HARD DECISIONS. YOU WON'T HAVE TO DO ANY OF THAT.

ALL *YOU* DO THEN IS PICK UP WHAT I TELL YOU TO, OK?

*HEY!* DID I *SAY* TO PICK UP *ME?!* NO, AS A MATTER OF FACT, I DIDN'T! GET AWAY FROM THAT TRASH CAN! *I'M* THE ORGANIZER! *HEY!*

I CLEANED MY STUPID ROOM! CAN I GO OUTSIDE NOW?!

THAT DIDN'T TAKE YOU VERY LONG. LET'S SEE WHAT KIND OF JOB YOU DID.

I DID A *GREAT* JOB! SEE? CAN I GO NOW?

YOUR ROOM LOOKS GOOD. NOW DID YOU STRAIGHTEN UP YOUR CLOSET LIKE I ASKED YOU TO?

AAUGH! DON'T OPEN THAA...

BACK TO WORK, KIDDO.

*YOU* MADE *THIS* MESS! *YOU* CLEAN IT UP!

WHACK

OUR FAVORITE GAMES ARE THE ONES WE DON'T UNDERSTAND!

YOU MISSED A WICKET! NO GOAL! NO GOAL!

HELP! A BEE! A BEE! RUN FOR YOUR LIFE!

HOBBES! DID YOU SEE IT?? IT WAS THE BIGGEST BEE IN THE WORLD! IT WAS THE SIZE OF A KAISER ROLL! IT MUST'VE WEIGHED 70 POUNDS!

IT SOUNDED LIKE A HELICOPTER, AND ITS STINGER WAS LIKE A HARPOON! IT MUST'VE BEEN A KILLER DEATH BEE! MAN, I'M LUCKY IT DIDN'T GET ME!

LIFE IN THE GREAT SUBURBAN OUTBACK IS CERTAINLY FRAUGHT WITH PERIL.

IF YOU'D SEEN IT, YOU'D HAVE BEEN SCARED, TOO.

I CAN'T IMAGINE MASTERING THE SKILLS INVOLVED HERE WITHOUT A CLEARER UNDERSTANDING OF WHO'S GOING TO BE IMPRESSED.

I SAW THE MAN IN THE MOON TONIGHT.

MM.

I DIDN'T KNOW THE MOON MADE FACES.

THAT'S "PHASES."

90

# CALViN AND HOBBES

by WATTERSON

AHHHH...

UH-OH. SOMETHING IS SERIOUSLY WRONG HERE.

THE LAWS OF PERSPECTIVE HAVE BEEN REPEALED!

OBJECTS NO LONGER DIMINISH IN SIZE WITH DISTANCE!

LINES DO NOT CONVERGE TOWARD ANY POINT ON THE HORIZON!

ALL SPATIAL RELATIONSHIPS ARE LOST! IT'S IMPOSSIBLE TO JUDGE WHERE ANY-THING IS! OH NO!

CALVIN, QUIT RUNNING AROUND AND CRASHING INTO THINGS, OR I'LL SELL YOU TO THE MONKEY HOUSE!

...AND NOW SHE'S LOST PERSPECTIVE.

THE GIANT PTERANODON HOPS TO THE EDGE OF THE CLIFF.

THERE HE SPREADS HIS BAT-LIKE WINGS AND TAKES TO THE AIR! SOARING HIGH OVER THE PREHISTORIC VALLEY, THE PTERANODON IS TRULY A MAJESTIC SIGHT!

THAT'S IT, THINK MAJESTIC!

I'M THINKING WE SHOULD'VE PICKED A SMALLER CLIFF!

IT'S TOO DARN HOT OUT HERE.

YOU COULD GO WADING IN THE CREEK.

THIS WATER IS TOO DARN COLD.

YOU COULD GO SIT IN THE SHADE THEN.

THIS SHADE IS TOO DARN DARK.

YOU COULD GO SIT IN YOUR ROOM WITH THE WINDOWS SHUT AND THE FAN AND LIGHTS ON.

THAT'S WHAT I WAS DOING WHEN MOM THREW ME OUT HERE.

I WAS KIDDING.

GIVE ME SOME COOKIES, OR I SOAK YOU WITH THIS WATER BALLOON!

WHY, YOU LITTLE THUG! DON'T YOU THREATEN YOUR MOTHER! AND DON'T EVEN *THINK* ABOUT THROWING THAT IN THE HOUSE!

OUT! OUT!

I'LL BET I'D HAVE GOTTEN SOME COOKIES IF I HAD FILLED THIS WITH *PAINT*.

# Calvin and Hobbes

by WATTERSON

YOU CAN TAKE THE TIGER OUT OF THE JUNGLE, BUT YOU CAN'T TAKE THE JUNGLE OUT OF THE TIGER!

THE QUESTION *IS*, HOW CAN YOU GET THE TIGER *BACK* IN THE JUNGLE?

IT'S JULY ALREADY! OH NO! OH NO!

WHAT HAPPENED TO JUNE?! SUMMER VACATION IS SLIPPING THROUGH OUR FINGERS LIKE GRAINS OF SAND!

IT'S GOING TOO FAST! WE'VE GOT TO HOARD OUR FREEDOM AND HAVE MORE FUN! TIME RUSHES ON! HELP! HELP!

I DON'T THINK I WANT TO BE HERE AT THE END OF AUGUST.

AAUGH! IT'S A HALF-HOUR LATER THAN IT WAS HALF AN HOUR AGO! RUN! RUN!

MOM TOOK ME TO THE LIBRARY TODAY, DAD.

THAT'S NICE. DID YOU GET OUT A BOOK?

YEP. IT'S GREAT! I HAD NO IDEA BOOKS COULD BE SO MUCH FUN.

AND YOU'LL LEARN THINGS, TOO.

I'LL SAY! MY BOOK SAYS THAT THIS ONE WASP LAYS ITS EGG ON A SPIDER, SO WHEN THE EGG HATCHES, THE LARVA EATS THE SPIDER, SAVING THE VITAL ORGANS FOR LAST, SO THE SPIDER STAYS ALIVE WHILE IT'S BEING DEVOURED!

GROSS, HUH?

ISN'T THERE A STREET CORNER WHERE HE COULD HANG OUT INSTEAD?

AND COLOR PICTURES, TOO! WANT TO SEE 'EM?

I'M DESTINED FOR GREATNESS, I JUST KNOW IT. "CALVIN THE GREAT," THEY'LL CALL ME.

AND THINK HOW LUCKY YOU'LL BE! YOU'LL GET TO TELL EVERYONE HOW YOU KNEW ME AS A KID! WHAT A PRIVILEGE!

IN FACT, ALL THE PAPERS AND MAGAZINES WILL PROBABLY WANT TO INTERVIEW YOU TO FIND OUT WHAT I'M REALLY LIKE.

AND BOY, WILL YOU HAVE TO COUGH UP TO KEEP ME QUIET.

AND WHAT'S THAT SUPPOSED TO MEAN?!

DO RE MI FA
SO LA TI DO

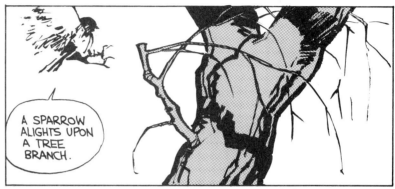

A SPARROW ALIGHTS UPON A TREE BRANCH.

BUT THIS IS NO *ORDI-NARY* SPARROW! THIS IS A *SONG* SPARROW!

SWAYING GENTLY IN THE BREEZE, HE PREPARES TO BURST FORTH IN RAPTUROUS MELODY!

ON TOP OF SPA-GHETTI

ALL COVERED WITH CHEEEESE, I LOST MY POOR MEEEATBALL, WHEN...

# CALVIN AND HOBBES by WATTERSON

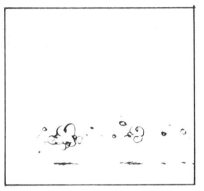

YOU'RE OUT!

I THINK THE BASES ARE TOO DARN FAR APART.

AHH, YOU'RE JUST A BIG SISSY.

# CALVIN and HOBBES

by WATTERSON

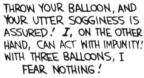

OFF TO WORK, EH, DAD?

YEP.

IT SURE IS A NICE DAY. THE KIND OF DAY JUST MADE FOR SITTING UNDER A TREE AND READING A GOOD NOVEL COVER TO COVER, DON'T YOU THINK?

TOO BAD THAT'S A LUXURY AT YOUR AGE. WELL, MAYBE YOU CAN DO IT WHEN YOU'RE 65. I'M SURE YOU'LL BE THAT OLD BEFORE YOU KNOW IT. ENJOY YOUR DAY AT WORK.

DAD SURE IS SURLY IN THE MORNINGS.

YOU KNOW WHAT'S WEIRD? I DON'T REMEMBER MUCH OF ANYTHING UNTIL I WAS THREE YEARS OLD.

HALF OF MY LIFE IS A COMPLETE BLANK! I MUST'VE BEEN BRAINWASHED!

GOOD HEAVENS, WHAT KIND OF SICKO WOULD BRAINWASH AN INFANT?! AND WHAT DID I KNOW THAT SOMEONE WANTED ME TO FORGET??

BOY, AM I MYSTERIOUS.

I SEEM TO RECALL YOU SPENT MOST OF THE TIME BURPING UP.

MOM! THERE'S A BIG HORSEFLY ON THE BACK OF YOUR HEAD! DON'T MOVE! I'LL GET IT!

IS IT STILL THERE? YOU DIDN'T MOVE, DID YOU?

GET AWAY FROM ME!

I PERFORMED A SCIENTIFIC EXPERIMENT TODAY.

YOU KNOW HOW MAPS ALWAYS SHOW NORTH AS UP AND SOUTH AS DOWN? I WANTED TO SEE IF THAT WAS TRUE OR NOT.

WHAT DID YOU FIND OUT?

NOT MUCH. YOUR COMPASS DIDN'T SURVIVE THE TRIP SOUTH FROM THE TOP OF THE TREE.

*MY* COMPASS?!

LET ME KNOW WHEN YOU GET A NEW ONE. MY JUNIOR SCIENTIST BOOK SAYS NOT TO GET DISCOURAGED BY TEMPORARY SETBACKS.

I'VE BEEN THINKING. YOU KNOW HOW BORING DAD IS? MAYBE IT'S A BIG PHONY ACT!

MAYBE AFTER HE PUTS US TO BED, DAD DONS SOME WEIRD COSTUME AND GOES OUT FIGHTING CRIME! MAYBE THIS WHOLE "DAD" STUFF IS JUST A SECRET IDENTITY!

MAYBE THE MAYOR CALLS DAD ON A SECRET HOT LINE WHENEVER THE CITY'S IN TROUBLE! MAYBE DAD'S A MASKED SUPERHERO!

IF THAT'S TRUE HE SHOULD DRIVE A COOLER CAR.

I KNOW. OURS DOESN'T EVEN HAVE A CASSETTE DECK.

THERE'S THE STEGOSAURUS OUT FRONT! THERE'S THE NATURAL HISTORY MUSEUM! HOORAY!

I CAN'T WAIT TO SEE ALL THE DINOSAURS! C'MON, LET'S HURRY!

IT'S CERTAINLY BEEN A WHILE SINCE WE'VE BEEN HERE, HASN'T IT?

AT THE MUSEUM'S REQUEST, YES.

OH, THAT'S RIGHT. CALVIN, NO BITING PEOPLE THIS TIME, REMEMBER?

RROWRR

# CaLViN and HobbEs by WATTERSON

THERE! A FULL PITCHER OF "CALVIN'S CURATIVE ELIXIR"! WE'LL CHARGE PEOPLE A BUCK A GLASS AND GET RICH!

BUT THAT'S JUST DIRTY WATER FROM THE DRAINAGE DITCH! THERE ARE LEAVES IN IT!

"FORTIFIED WITH CHLOROPHYLL," WE'LL SAY.

NOBODY'S GOING TO PAY TO DRINK THAT! ANYONE CAN SEE IT'S FILTHY! IT'S SLUDGE!

HMM... MAYBE YOU'RE RIGHT.

PITCHER OF PLAGUE
Calvin's DEBILITATING DISEASE DRINK!
$1.00 NOT TO HAVE ANY

I'VE DECIDED NOT TO GO TO SCHOOL THIS FALL.

I DON'T NEED AN EDUCATION. I DON'T NEED TO LEARN THINGS. I DON'T NEED TO DEVELOP SKILLS. IT'S TOO MUCH TROUBLE.

HOW ARE YOU GOING TO MAKE IT IN THE WORLD IF YOU DON'T KNOW ANYTHING AND YOU DON'T HAVE ANY SKILLS?!

I'LL GO ON TALK SHOWS AND HYPE MYSELF.

UGHH, THERE ARE TIMES WHEN I HATE OWNING A HOUSE. ALL THE MAINTENANCE!

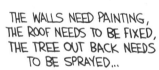

THE WALLS NEED PAINTING, THE ROOF NEEDS TO BE FIXED, THE TREE OUT BACK NEEDS TO BE SPRAYED...

IT SEEMS LIKE THE WHOLE PLACE IS FALLING APART.

... AND WHAT ISN'T FALLING APART IS BEING ACTIVELY DESTROYED!

# calvin and hobbes

by WATTERSON

A 30-TON BRONTOSAURUS

... IS ABOUT TO FACE A PREMATURE EXTINCTION!

THE ALLOSAURUS, FEARSOME PREDATOR OF THE JURASSIC, STALKS HIS PREY!

THE HERD OF BRONTOSAURS IS UNAWARE OF HIS PRESENCE!

SPOTTING A STRAGGLER, THE ALLOSAURUS LUNGES!

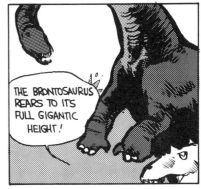

THE BRONTOSAURUS REARS TO ITS FULL GIGANTIC HEIGHT!

WHAT INDUCES AN ALLOSAURUS TO ATTACK A MONSTER MORE THAN TWICE HIS OWN SIZE??

I'M HUNGRY!

THE HAMBURGERS ARE COOKING! NOW GET OFF ME!

117

CALVIN THE HUMMINGBIRD ZIPS BY WITH A LOUD WHIR!

ALTHOUGH SMALL, HE PUTS OUT TREMENDOUS ENERGY. TO HOVER, HIS WINGS BEAT HUNDREDS OF TIMES EACH SECOND!

WHAT FUELS THIS INCREDIBLE METABOLISM? CONCENTRATED SUGAR WATER! HE DRINKS HALF HIS WEIGHT A DAY!

...PREFERABLY LOADED WITH CAFFEINE.

ARE YOU DRINKING MORE SODA POP?!

SLURRPP

"ONCE UPON A TIME THERE WAS..."

HOLD IT.

WHAT'S THE MATTER?

HAS THIS BOOK BEEN A BEST SELLER? HAS THE AUTHOR WON A PULITZER? DID THE NEW YORK TIMES LIKE IT?

I ONLY WANT STORIES THAT COME HIGHLY RECOMMENDED. ARE THERE ANY LAUDATORY QUOTES ON THE DUST JACKET?

AHEM..."ONCE UPON A TIME THERE WAS A NOISY KID WHO STARTED GOING TO BED WITHOUT A STORY."

HAS THIS BOOK BEEN MADE INTO A MOVIE? COULD WE BE WATCHING THIS ON VIDEO?

WHAT ARE YOU DOING?

I'M PRACTICING MY SNEERS.

THERE'S NOTHING LIKE A GOOD SNEER TO DRY UP CONVERSATION. HOW'S MINE LOOK?

AWFUL!

THANKS. WITH THIS SNEER, I HOPE TO BE AN UNBEARABLE BURDEN AT ANY SOCIAL OCCASION.

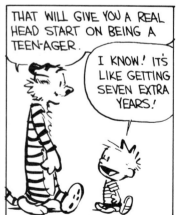

THAT WILL GIVE YOU A REAL HEAD START ON BEING A TEEN-AGER.

I KNOW! IT'S LIKE GETTING SEVEN EXTRA YEARS!

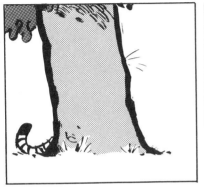

OK, THE FIRST THING OUR ROBOT NEEDS IS A HEAD.

SHOULD WE USE A COFFEE CAN?

NO, THAT'S TOO SMALL. THE HEAD HAS TO HOLD THIS TAPE RECORDER. SEE, I'VE MADE RECORDINGS FOR THE ROBOT'S VOICE!

REALLY?

SURE! THIS WAY, OUR ROBOT NOT ONLY COMMUNICATES, BUT WE CAN ALSO "PROGRAM" HIM TO HAVE THE PROPER PERSONALITY!

PERSONALITY?

RIGHT. ROBOTS SHOULD BE *RESPECTFUL.*

*CLICK* HOW MAY I EASE YOUR LIFE, OH GRAND EXALTED MASTER?

HEY, DAD, I'M INVENTING A ROBOT. CAN YOU GET ME A PATENT?

YOU INVENTED A ROBOT?

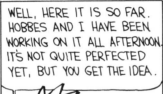

WELL, HERE IT IS SO FAR. HOBBES AND I HAVE BEEN WORKING ON IT ALL AFTERNOON. IT'S NOT QUITE PERFECTED YET, BUT YOU GET THE IDEA.

HMM... WHAT DOES IT DO?

THAT'S THE PROBLEM. WE HAVEN'T FIGURED OUT HOW TO MAKE IT DO WHAT WE WANT.

DON'T GET DISCOURAGED. YOUR MOM AND I GOT THE SAME RESULTS AFTER WORKING ON *YOU* FOR SIX *YEARS.*

HAR HAR. MY ATTORNEY IS A COMEDIAN.

WELL, HOBBES, WE MIGHT AS WELL GIVE UP. I CAN'T FIGURE OUT HOW TO MAKE A ROBOT. THIS ONE DOESN'T DO ANYTHING.

IT'S PAST YOUR BEDTIME, CALVIN. YOU'LL HAVE TO LEAVE YOUR TOYS FOR TOMORROW.

OK, MOM. OUR ROBOT WASN'T WORKING OUT ANYWAY.

GOSH, AND WE SPENT ALL DAY ON IT, TOO. I THOUGHT FOR SURE OUR ROBOT WOULD SAVE US FROM MAKING THE BED.

AND IN A WAY, HE *DID!*

HEY, YEAH! WE'RE GENIUSES!

YOUR MOM SURE WAS CHEERFUL THIS MORNING.

HMPH.

I'VE NEVER SEEN HER HUMMING AND SASHAYING AROUND THE KITCHEN LIKE THAT.

HMPH.

HOW LONG HAVE WE BEEN WAITING FOR THE BUS NOW?

ABOUT TWO AND A HALF HOURS.

*I* THINK MOM PUT ME OUT HERE THIS EARLY ON *PURPOSE*.

HI, CALVIN! AREN'T YOU EXCITED ABOUT GOING TO SCHOOL? LOOK AT ALL THESE GREAT SCHOOL SUPPLIES I GOT! I LOVE HAVING NEW NOTEBOOKS AND STUFF!

ALL *I'VE* GOT TO SAY IS THEY'RE NOT MAKING *ME* LEARN ANY FOREIGN LANGUAGES! IF ENGLISH IS GOOD ENOUGH FOR *ME*, THEN BY GOLLY, IT'S GOOD ENOUGH FOR THE *REST* OF THE WORLD!

EVERYONE SHOULD SPEAK ENGLISH OR JUST SHUT UP, THAT'S WHAT *I* SAY!

YOU SHOULD MAYBE CHECK THE CHEMICAL CONTENT OF YOUR BREAKFAST CEREAL.

THEY CAN MAKE ME GO UNTIL GRADE EIGHT, AND THEN, *FFFT*, I'M OUTTA HERE!

CALVIN, WOULD YOU LEAD THE CLASS IN THE PLEDGE OF ALLEGIANCE?

NO!!

WHAT DID THE SUPREME COURT DECIDE ABOUT THAT? IS THIS A PRAYER? DON'T YOU HAVE TO READ ME MY RIGHTS? I DON'T KEEP UP WITH THIS STUFF! I'M JUST A KID!

I'M ONLY HERE BECAUSE MY PARENTS MAKE ME GO! I DON'T WANT TO BE A TEST CASE! I DON'T EVEN KNOW WHAT COURT DISTRICT I'M IN! CALL ON SOMEONE ELSE!

CALVIN?

＊SIGHHHH＊ I CAN'T BELIEVE IT'S NOT EVEN 8:15 YET.

THE FEARLESS SPACEMAN SPIFF IS BEING PURSUED ACROSS THE GALAXY BY DREADED SCUM BEINGS!

THEY'RE GAINING! SPIFF'S ONLY CHANCE TO LOSE THEM IS TO RELEASE A GIANT SMOKE CLOUD BEHIND HIS SPACECRAFT! OUR HERO THROWS THE LEVER!

HEH HEH... JUST UH, CLAPPING THE ERASERS, HEH HEH... (COUGH)

YOU AGAIN?

*SIGHHHH* I CAN'T BELIEVE IT'S NOT EVEN 8:30 YET.

WHAT A DAY.

I'M HO-O--AAAH!

KAPOINWW!!!

THINGS GET SO DARN QUIET WHEN YOU'RE NOT AROUND.

THERE'S GOING TO BE SOME RUCKUS NOW, BUDDY-BOY!

IS IT? IT IS! IT'S SATURDAY! OH BOY!

NO SCHOOL! NO HOMEWORK! JUST CARTOONS AND FUN THE WHOLE DAY LONG!

HOORAY!

TURN ON THE TV! GET OUT THE CEREAL!

IT'S SAAAAT URDAY!

BONK

BONK

BONK

YOU'RE GETTING UP?? IT'S BARELY LIGHT OUT!

I'M GOING TO THE OFFICE AND GET SOME SLEEP.

# CALVIN and HOBBES

by WATTERSON

CALVIN?

CALVIN?

CALVIN!

HMM... THE ENGINE'S MAKING FUNNY NOISES..

SPACEMAN SPIFF IS GOING DOWN OVER PLANET GORK!

ZOUNDS! THE PLANET IS INHABITED! AN ALIEN METROPOLIS OPENS UP BEFORE OUR HERO'S EYES!

SPIFF'S STABILIZERS REFUSE TO RESPOND! OUR HERO IS GOING TO CRASH!

THIS SPELLS DISASTER!

CALVIN!

"UH... D...I...S...A... S...T...E...R.

VERY GOOD. I'M GLAD YOU WERE PAYING ATTENTION.

YES! ONCE AGAIN THE INCREDIBLE SPACEMAN SPIFF BEATS ALL ODDS TO SAVE THE DAY!

YOU MAY SIT DOWN, CALVIN.

125

UH OH, CALVIN THE REPTILE IS IN TROUBLE!

AS AN ECTOTHERM, HIS BODY RELIES ON THE ENVIRONMENT TO WARM OR COOL ITS TEMPERATURE.

NOW THAT IT'S COLDER OUTSIDE, CALVIN'S BODY TEMPERATURE FALLS AND HE BECOMES SLUGGISH! HE'LL GO INTO TORPOR IF HE CAN'T FIND A WARM PLACE TO LIE!

LEAVE THE THERMOSTAT ALONE, AND PUT ON A SWEATER IF YOU'RE COLD.

I...I DON'T HAVE THE EN..ENERGY!

I HEARD THAT BIG CATS DON'T PURR.

THAT'S TRUE. WE'RE TOO FIERCE AND FEROCIOUS. WE DON'T EVER PURR.

WELL WHAT DO YOU CALL THE NOISE YOU MAKE WHEN YOU GET YOUR TUMMY RUBBED?!

GROWLING FRIENDLY-LIKE.

CALVIN, YOUR MOM AND I LOOKED OVER YOUR REPORT CARD, AND WE THINK YOU COULD BE DOING BETTER.

BUT I DON'T LIKE SCHOOL.

WHY NOT? YOU LIKE TO READ AND YOU LIKE TO LEARN. I KNOW YOU DO.

I MEAN, YOU'VE READ EVERY DINOSAUR BOOK EVER WRITTEN, AND YOU'VE LEARNED A LOT, RIGHT? READING AND LEARNING ARE FUN.

YEAH..

SO WHY DON'T YOU LIKE SCHOOL?

WE DON'T READ ABOUT DINOSAURS.

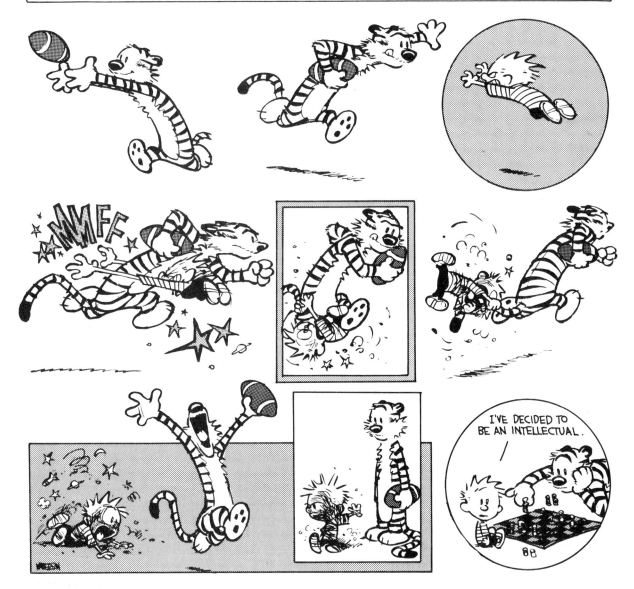

# The End